Ransom Neutron Stars
G B H
by Jill Atkins
Illustrated by Richard Williams

Published by Ransom Publishing Ltd.
Unit 7, Brocklands Farm, West Meon, Hampshire GU32 1JN, UK
www.ransom.co.uk

ISBN   978 178591 429 4
First published in 2017

G B H

Jill Atkins

Illustrated by Richard Williams

Dan was in his bedroom.

There was a ring on the bell.

It was the cops.

There was a cop car in the road

and a cop on the step.

"Are you Dan Brown?" said the cop.

"Yes."

"Is Mum or Dad in?"

"No."

"We have come to arrest you."

"What for?"

"GBH."

"GBH?"

Dan was upset. "Not me!"

"You must come with us," said the cop.

Dan got in the cop car
and they went to the cop shop.

When they got there, Dan was led into a room.

A smart cop sat at a desk.

"Sit down," she said.
Dan sat down.

"Are you Dan Brown?"
"Yes," said Dan. "What is it?"

"Kevin Green said you all hit him. Said you hit him hard. You and Justin Black and Krish Sharma. You all hit Kevin Green next to the chip shop."

"No."

"Did you hit him, Dan?"

"No!"

"Did you kick him?"

"No, I did not!"

"So you must tell us what did happen
then. We need the facts."

Dan felt cross.

Kevin Green was a creep.

Dan did not like him, but he did not hit
him or kick him.

"Justin Black is in the next room," said the cop. "He will tell us."

Will Justin tell the cops the facts?

"And Krish Sharma is in a room as well. He will tell us."

*Will Krish tell the cops **all** the facts?*

Dan bit his lip.

"It was Justin," he said.

"Justin Black? *Just* Justin?"

"Yes."

"Not you or Krish Sharma?" said the smart cop.

"No. I was there and Krish was there, but we did not hit or kick Kevin."

Dan felt bad. Justin was his best pal, but they were the facts.

"Kevin hit Justin," said Dan. "So Justin hit Kevin back. Then they had a fight. It was a punch-up and Kevin was hurt."

The cop stood up.

"I will see what Justin and Krish tell us," she said, and she left the room.

Dan sat still. He was mad with Kevin, but he felt bad with himself.

Then the cop was back in the room.

"Thank you, Dan," she said. "Now I have all the facts. It was not GBH. It was just a fight with Justin and Kevin. You are OK."

Dan was glad. He felt good.

Now the cops had all the facts.
It was not his problem.

"Can I go?" he said with a sniff.

"Yes. You can go," said the smart cop.

"Can I ring my mum to ask her to pick me up?" said Dan.

"Yes," said the smart cop. "You can ring from the main desk."

Dan's mum got him in the car.

"That Kevin Green is a pest," she said.
"He is a clown. Keep away from him
from now on."

"I will," said Dan, as they left the cop shop.

"But I have things to finish with Kevin," Dan said to himself. "He is a creep and a prat. Next week I will sort him out."

Have you read?

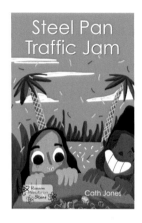

Steel Pan Traffic Jam

by Cath Jones

Platform 7

by Stephen Rickard

Have you read?

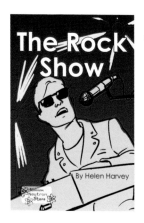

The Rock Show

by Helen Harvey

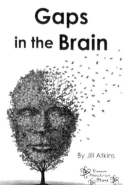

Gaps in the Brain

by Jill Atkins

Ransom Neutron Stars

G B H
Word count **501**

Covers:
Letters and Sounds Phase 4

Phonics

Phonics 1 Not Pop, Not Rock Go to the Laptop Man Gus and the Tin of Ham	*Phonics 2* Deep in the Dark Woods Night Combat Ben's Jerk Chicken Van
Phonics 3 **G B H** Steel Pan Traffic Jam Platform 7	*Phonics 4* The Rock Show Gaps in the Brain New Kinds of Energy

Book bands

Pink Curry! Free Runners My Toys	*Red* Shopping with Zombies Into the Scanner Planting My Garden
Yellow Fit for Love The Lottery Ticket In the Stars	*Blue* Awesome ATAs Wolves The Giant Jigsaw
Green Fly, May FLY! How to Start Your Own Crazy Cult The Care Home	*Orange* Text Me The Last Soldier Best Friends